WHAT'S BLACK AND WHITE
AND READ ALL OVER?

THE SNOOPY ANNUAL!

This year's megamix contains the latest PEANUTS strips available for publication in book form, plus Charles Schulz's own selection of classic PEANUTS strips from the past. In addition, there are three brand new Snoopy stories and a special funny poem in which Snoopy goes golfing with good ol' Charlie Brown.

Still on the subject of humour, you can find out what Peppermint Patty has to tell her friends when she visits London with her Dad, and what Lucy has to say when everyone comes to her asking for advice. Both are hilarious!

On the information front, there's the lowdown on the French Foreign Legion, plus the gripping true story of Snoopy's famous flying adversary, the Red Baron.

For those of you who like to keep your brains busy, there's a great quiz all about children and three fiendish puzzles featuring Charlie Brown, Sally and Linus; for those of you who like to have busy hands, there are two mouth-watering recipes personally approved by Snoopy. All of which just leaves room to mention the two bound-in posters which should delight everyone's eye.

So what are you waiting for? Come on in, Joe Reader. The new SNOOPY ANNUAL is as cool as Snoopy's shades!

THE Snoopy ANNUAL

Created by
Charles M. Schulz

Written by
Gordon Volke

ℛℛ
RAVETTE BOOKS

CONTENTS

Printed and bound for Ravette Books Limited, 3 Glenside Estate, Star Road, Partridge Green, Horsham, West Sussex RH13 8RA. An Egmont Company.
By Stige Arti Grafiche, Italy.

ISBN 1 85304 423 7

"Good evening, Sir," said Charlie Brown, hurrying out of the house with Snoopy's supperdish. "My name is Brown and I'm your waiter for tonight."

"Not again," thought Snoopy.

"Our special today, sir, is dog food," continued Charlie Brown.

"Not again," repeated Snoopy.

"Sir appears to be tired of this dish," exclaimed Charlie Brown. "I'll make it more interesting by serving it while standing on my head."

"Oh, no!" thought Snoopy, holding his head in his paws. "NOT AGAIN!"

Then Charlie Brown proceeded to tell a joke.

"Heard this one, Snoopy?" he grinned. "Why did the girl go to the party with a six-foot toadstool?"

"I don't know," thought Snoopy, shaking his head and holding out his paws. "Why *did* the girl go to the party with a six-foot toadstool?"

"Because," guffawed Charlie Brown, "he was a fungi to be with! HA, HA, HA, HA, HA!"

Snoopy waited several minutes while his master rolled around helplessly at his own joke.

"What am I doing here?" thought Snoopy.

7

After supper, Charlie Brown went to fly his kite.

"It'll get eaten by the kite-eating tree," thought Snoopy.

"It won't get eaten by the kite-eating tree," called Charlie Brown, "because I'm not going to launch it. YOU are!"

Before Snoopy knew what was happening, the kite string was thrust into his paws. At first, all went well. Snoopy assumed a smug expression as the kite rose higher and higher in the sky. Then a strong gust of wind lifted Snoopy clean off the ground.

"You're too light for kite-flying, Snoopy!" yelled Charlie Brown.

"*Now* he tells me," groaned Snoopy.

Snoopy flew through the air with his arms stretched out in front of him.

"You look like Superbeagle," called Charlie Brown.

"This is no time for wisecracks!" thought Snoopy.

Snoopy crashed into the branches of a tree. The kite floated gently to the ground.

"Now *I'm* being eaten by the Kite-eating tree!" wailed Snoopy.

Charlie Brown hurried over and began beckoning urgently.

"Get down, Snoopy," he yelled.

"What's the hurry?" wondered Snoopy, starting to crawl along a branch. Suddenly, there was a loud SNAP! The branch broke and Snoopy fell head-first onto the ground.

"OWCH!" he yelped.

Snoopy expected to be helped to his feet. Instead, Charlie Brown stood in front of him, giving a sickly smile. Snoopy soon saw why. The Little Red-Haired Girl was passing by.

"Please excuse my dog," said Charlie Brown. "He can't help looking foolish. He's simple-minded."

"That does it!" thought Snoopy.

As Charlie Brown carried his kite back home, Snoopy set off in the opposite direction.

"The Round-Headed Kid has insulted me once too often," muttered Snoopy. "I'm leaving!"

Snoopy marched down the road and knocked on the door of the Van Pelt household. Linus answered, and Snoopy assumed his most helpless and pathetic-looking expression.

"Come in, Snoopy," said Linus.

Snoopy shot in through the door and jumped onto the beanbag chair in front of the television.

"I take it you want to stay," smiled Linus.

"I sure do!" thought Snoopy.

Snoopy was just dozing off when a sudden weight descended on him from above.

"What's this dog doing in my chair?" shrieked Lucy.

"It isn't your chair," replied Linus. "It's *our* chair."

"Big sisters have priority in all things," snapped Lucy, tipping the chair up. "Scram, Snoopy. I want to watch TV."

Snoopy picked himself up from the carpet and headed for the front door.

"I can't live here," thought Snoopy. "Lucy's too crabby."

Snoopy moved on to Schroeder's house. The back door was open, so he went inside and curled up on a black and white cushion beside Schroeder's piano. Schroeder did not see him when he arrived for his daily piano practice.

DA-DA-DA-DAAH! DA-DA-DA-DAAH! Schroeder thumped out the opening chords of Beethoven's Fifth Symphony and Snoopy shot into the air like a space rocket being launched to the moon.

"What are you doing here, Snoopy?" exclaimed Schroeder.

"Trying to get some shuteye," thought Snoopy.

"I can feed you in about three hours time," said Schroeder. "That's how long I usually play my piano."

"See you," thought Snoopy, making for the door.

Snoopy made his way across town to Peppermint Patty's house.

"Patty's always nice to me," he thought. "She'll give me a good home."

Snoopy was right. Patty opened the door with a big, welcoming smile.

"My Dad and I have just finished supper," she said. "Would you like the leftovers?"

"With chocolate-chip cookies for desert and some ginger beer by the side?" wondered Snoopy.

"I think there are some chocolate-chip cookies in the larder," added Peppermint Patty, "and there's a bottle of ginger beer somewhere, too."

"I'm going to like it here," thought Snoopy.

After a delicious meal, Snoopy settled down for a nap. He was soon woken by a large hand ruffling his ears. Opening his eyes, he saw Peppermint Patty's Dad beaming down at him. For the next few minutes, Snoopy was patted and fondled and cooed at. Snoopy had never known such attention at home.

"I don't want any more, though!" he thought.

A soon as Patty's Dad had gone, Snoopy slipped out of the house and made his way back towards Charlie Brown's. His master was out looking for him.

"*There* you are, Snoopy!" exclaimed Charlie Brown. "Where have you been?"

"Finding out I want to stay with you," thought Snoopy.

Back home, Charlie Brown served Snoopy a late-night supper – and he stood on his head! This time, Snoopy did not mind. He ran over and gave Charlie Brown a hug. Afterwards, when he told Woodstock of his adventures, the little bird asked why Snoopy had left the comfort of Peppermint Patty's house.

"Her Dad called me a 'doggy'," explained Snoopy, "and that's the worst insult of all!"

HERE'S THE FIERCE SNOW SNAKE SNEAKING UP ON A VICTIM...

JUST THE OTHER DAY I WAS READING THAT THERE ISN'T SUCH A THING AS A SNOW SNAKE...

1-17

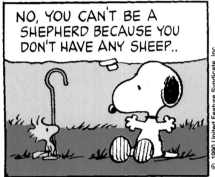

NO, YOU CAN'T BE A SHEPHERD BECAUSE YOU DON'T HAVE ANY SHEEP..

1-20

BAA! I MUST BE OUT OF MY MIND..

SURE, WHY NOT?

1-22

WELL, PUT IT ON, AND LET ME SEE...

YES, IT DOES MAKE YOU LOOK TALLER

Truth may be stranger than fiction – unless I write the fiction!

11

I WONDER WHAT I CAN DO TO MAKE THAT LITTLE RED-HAIRED GIRL NOTICE ME..

MAYBE IF I WALK AROUND THE ROOM A BIT...I'LL BET SHE NOTICES ME NOW...

ESPECIALLY AFTER I GET MY SLEEVE CAUGHT IN THE PENCIL SHARPENER..

IF THAT LITTLE RED-HAIRED GIRL SEES ME STANDING HERE WITH MY SLEEVE CAUGHT IN THE PENCIL SHARPENER, SHE'LL THINK I'M THE DUMBEST PERSON IN THE WORLD

WHAT I HAVE TO DO IS WRIGGLE OUT OF MY SWEATER BUT STILL LOOK REAL COOL...

WHY DO WE HAVE TO STAND IN LINE FOR EVERYTHING?

WHAT'S THE HOLDUP?

PROBABLY AN OVERTURNED VEHICLE

PUSH 'IM OUT O'THERE

WHAT'S TAKING YOU SO LONG, CHARLES?

I LIKE A PENCIL WITH A FINE POINT..

YOU GOT THE SLEEVE OF YOUR SWEATER CAUGHT IN THE PENCIL SHARPENER?

WELL, WHAT DID YOU DO? HOW DID YOU GET IT OUT?

KIDS' STUFF

Charlie Brown and his friends are amongst the best-known children in the world. Here are a dozen questions about some other famous youngsters and the whole realm of childhood. Answers on page 58.

1

How old was Mozart when he began composing music?
(a) 5
(b) 10
(c) 15

2

Can you name the 4 children and the dog that make up Enid Blyton's 'Famous Five'.

3

Legend says that baby twins, brought up by a wolf, later founded the city of Rome. What are they called?
(a) Castor and Pollux
(b) Romulus and Remus
(c) Tom and Jerry

4

In 1212, thousands of children, led by Peter the Hermit, left Europe on a Crusade to win the Holy Land back by love rather than by force.
(a) True?
(b) False?

5

Who sailed down the Mississippi on a raft in a famous story by Mark Twain?
(a) Tom Sawyer
(b) Pudd'nhead Wilson
(c) Huckleberry Finn

6

Who is the President of the Save The Children Fund?
(a) The Queen
(b) Princess Margaret
(c) Princess Anne

14

10

Can you complete this well-known saying?
'The child is – – – – – – to the man.'

7

In pantomime, who is the 'boy who never grew up'?

11

As a tiny baby, Robin Hood was hidden away by the wizard Merlin for his own protection.
(a) True?
(b) False?

8

Who was the young leader of the pickpockets in 'Oliver Twist'?
(a) The Artful Dodger
(b) Dennis the Menace
(c) Scrooge

12

Who has a baby brother called Rerun?
(a) Charlie Brown and Sally
(b) Lucy and Linus
(c) Snoopy

9

In the 1830s and 40s, who stopped children having to work long hours in factories and mines?
(a) Charles Dickens
(b) Lord Shaftsbury
(c) Queen Victoria

FORT ZINDERNEUF REVISITED

When Snoopy and his friends assume the roles of Foreign Legionnaires, they join the ranks of an organisation whose image is as romantic as a Sahara sunset. In reality, though, the French Foreign Legion is a highly disciplined professional army working in a harsh and inhospitable terrain.

Picturepoint – London

Snoopy's Foreign Legion Factfile

The French 'Légion Étrangère' was founded in 1831 by King Louis-Philippe. Its original purpose was to guard the lands in Africa that France had taken as colonies.

The Legion's unofficial motto is 'Legio Patria Nostra' ('the Legion is our fatherland'). When a new recruit joins the force, he has to swear a special oath, not promising to serve France but to serve the Legion.

 In return for total loyalty, the French Foreign Legion promises to keep secret a volunteer's past. Hence it has always been a sanctuary for criminals escaping the law, heartbroken lovers and idealistic noblemen serving under false names.

 Most of the officers in the Legion are French, but the ordinary soldiers come from every country under the sun. After serving one five-year term of enlistment with good conduct, a Legionnaire becomes eligible for French citizenship.

 The Legion has always been prohibited from being stationed in mainland France during peacetime, but it did see active service on home soil during World War 1 and World War 2.

 Up until 1962, the organisation's head-quarters was at Sidi bel Abbes in Algeria. When that country became independent, the Legion relocated to a military base in Corsica with a command HQ in metropolitan France.

An officer in modern Foreign Legion uniform. Note the black kepi cap like Snoopy's. Ordinary soldiers wear white hats.

NO, YOU CAN GIVE A VALENTINE TO SOMEONE ANY WAY YOU WANT TO..

YOU CAN HAND IT TO THEM, OR MAIL IT OR GIVE IT TO THEM ANY WAY YOU WANT TO...

© 1990 United Feature Syndicate, Inc.

2-14

I SENT THIRTY VALENTINES, AND DIDN'T GET EVEN ONE..

2-15

I MEAN, WHAT COULD BE WORSE THAN THAT?

© 1990 United Feature Syndicate, Inc.

BONK..

9-15

© 1990 United Feature Syndicate, Inc.

THEN AGAIN, MAYBE THE ONLY REAL LOVE IS BETWEEN A BOY AND HIS DOG..

I COULD HAVE TOLD YOU THAT A LONG TIME AGO... ARE THERE ANY MORE COOKIES LEFT?

SO WHEN WE GET TO FORT ZINDERNEUF, WE'LL HAVE TO GIVE A REPORT ON WHAT WE SAW WHILE ON PATROL..

9-18

NO, WE WON'T TELL THEM THAT WE WERE FOLLOWED BY A BEACH BALL..

SCHULZ

© 1990 United Feature Syndicate, Inc.

WELL, GIVE IT A GOOD KICK... MAYBE IT'LL STOP FOLLOWING US..

9-19

SCHULZ

© 1990 United Feature Syndicate, Inc.

IT'S VERY EMBARRASSING FOR A SQUAD OF TOUGH LÉGIONNAIRES TO BE FOLLOWED ACROSS THE DESERT BY A BEACH BALL..

9-20

ESPECIALLY WHEN IT GETS TIRED, AND I HAVE TO CARRY IT..

SCHULZ

© 1990 United Feature Syndicate, Inc.

HERE'S THE WORLD FAMOUS SERGEANT OF THE FOREIGN LEGION CAMPING OUT IN THE DESERT WITH HIS TROOPS..

THE NIGHTS ARE COLD AND LONELY...

© 1990 United Feature Syndicate, Inc.

WHO WANTS TO CUDDLE UP WITH A BEACH BALL?

HEE HEE HEE HEE

9-21

SCHULZ

All things shall pass, especially when I'm in goal!

CHARLIE BROWN'S FIND THE GANG PUZZLE

This grid contains the names of 10 of Charlie Brown's friends. To find them, you have to use the code at the bottom of the page to fill in all the letters. Then look for the names and shade them in. They are only spelt across or up and down.

One has been done for you and the solution is on page 58.

6	4	13	24	2	18	26	12	13	22
8	15	26	16	23	20	19	10	1	16
19	3	8	18	15	5	4	5	18	9
14	16	22	5	15	25	12	14	3	7
15	2	7	23	4	13	21	24	9	16
15	12	3	11	19	8	3	18	5	5
16	9	16	1	20	20	25	8	26	14
25	14	19	14	15	22	13	21	16	6
4	21	18	23	3	19	1	12	12	25
14	19	16	9	11	5	10	13	21	23

1	2	3	4	5	6	7	8	9	10	11	12	13	14	15	16	17	18	19	20	21	22	23	24	25	26
a	b	c	d	e	f	g	h	i	j	k	l	m	n	o	p	q	r	s	t	u	v	w	x	y	z

24

THE HOUSE
THAT JOE BUILT

Snoopy was feeling creative.

"Shall I write another novel?" he wondered. "It could be about a weather forecaster and begin, 'It was a dark and storm-force eight veering south-westerly night.' Or I could paint a stunning abstract picture – something like 'Supperdish with Magnolias.' How about some music? I could compose a stirring orchestral piece called 'March of the Chocolate-Chip Cookies.'

None of these ideas really appealed to Snoopy.

"They're not exciting enough," he murmured. "I fancy something practical."

Suddenly, Snoopy's eyes fell upon some bricks stacked in the corner of the garden. They had been thrown at him on various occasions by World War Two, the ferocious cat next-door.

"I'll create something beautiful with those," thought Snoopy.

Before he started work, Snoopy hurried indoors and fetched his baseball cap. He also put on an old pair of spectacles without any lenses and stuck a plastic bubble-blowing pipe in his mouth. Finally, he borrowed a model telescope from Charlie Brown's toybox. He took the telescope out into the garden and used it to survey the lie of the land.

"I'll site my new structure here," thought Joe Builder.

25

Using his front paws, Snoopy began digging the foundations.

"HOI!" yelled a voice. Looking round, Snoopy saw Charlie Brown standing with several divots of mud on his head.

"The Round-Headed Kid *is* the salt of the earth," thought Snoopy.

Charlie Brown was not amused.

"Stop pawing great holes in the lawn, Snoopy!" he yelled.

"Okay," thought Snoopy, fetching a spade.

Charlie Brown snatched it away.

"Dig your holes somewhere else, please," he hissed.

"Christopher Wren didn't have these problems," thought Snoopy, marching away.

Snoopy started erecting his building further down the garden.

"Do you have planning permission for that?" called another voice.

It was Lucy! She marched in through the back gate, looking bossier and even more important than ever. Snoopy ignored her.

"I said," repeated Lucy, tapping Snoopy on the shoulder, "do you have planning permission for this structure?"

Snoopy shrugged his shoulders.

"Then you'll have to take it down," said Lucy, folding her arms. "It's taking light from neighbouring gardens and ruining the skyline. As Junior Preservation Officer for the area, I order you to remove this eyesore."

Snoopy shook his head.

"Don't argue with me, Snoopy," bellowed Lucy, kicking over his line of bricks. "If you won't do the job, I'll do it for you!"

Snoopy fled as the bricks flew in all directions.

"Nothing worse than a crabby official!" he thought.

Snoopy set to work on a patch of waste ground beyond the garden. He had just completed a head-high rectangle of bricks when Linus arrived.

"Are you using Flemish Bond or Stretcher Bond?" asked Linus.

Snoopy stared at him blankly.

"I'm just sticking one brick on top of another," he thought. "Is that James Bond?"

"You can't build like that," continued Linus, taking down all Snoopy's handiwork. "Brick buildings are one of the most permanent structures known to Man provided the bricks are laid properly."

Snoopy waited patiently while Linus gave him a brick-laying lesson.

"When he's gone," thought Snoopy, "I'll do it my way."

Finally, as the sun began to set, Snoopy completed his masterpiece. He lay blissfully on his new, brick-built doghouse. "Creativity is what separates the dog from other species," he sighed.

A rumble from his tummy reminded Snoopy that it was suppertime. He hurried back to the house where Charlie Brown was just placing his supperdish dish beside his wooden doghouse.

"There's a hole here," cried Charlie Brown.

"Doesn't matter," thought Snoopy, booting the doghouse, "I'll make it bigger!"

"What *is* the matter with you today?" asked Charlie Brown, looking at Snoopy who stood with his arms folded and grin stretching from ear to ear.

"Being a dog of property gives you confidence," thought Snoopy.

After supper, Snoopy collected all his belongings and piled them into a wheelbarrow. He found things he had even forgotten he possessed, like a Joni James record and his collection of antique supperdishes.

"My oldest supperdish is from the Victorian era," thought Snoopy.

By the time everything was loaded, the wheelbarrow looked like a miniature mountain and, when Snoopy tried to push it, things kept falling off and hitting him on the head.

"They reckon moving house is one of life's most stressful experiences," thought Snoopy, "and now I know why!"

Snoopy's new home had just come into view when Woodstock flew down and perched on top of Snoopy's possession, squawking urgently.

"Nothing's wrong, Woodstock," laughed Snoopy. "I'm just going up-market to a more desirable residence."

Woodstock, however, continued to chirp and flap his wings in an unhappy manner. Then he flew down and perched on Snoopy's shoulder so he could twitter in his ear.

"What?" yelled Snoopy. "I've got SQUATTERS!"

Snoopy rushed over and peered inside his brick doghouse. It was true! There was movement inside it! Snoopy took one look at the new occupants and marched back to his wheelbarrow.

"The move's off," he told Woodstock, "I'm going back to Charlie Brown's,"

Woodstock perched on top of the wooden doghouse, watching Snoopy unloading all his things.

"I had to let the squatters stay, Woodstock," explained Snoopy.

"They were homeless, and my brick doghouse was purpose-built for their needs."

Woodstock gave a questioning twitter.

"Who were they?" translated Snoopy, giving a kindly smile.

"The Three Little Pigs!"

Postcards

from Patty

Recently, Peppermint Patty visited London with her Dad. These are the postcards she sent home to her friends. As always, Patty has got some of her facts wrong. Can you spot her mistakes? The correct information is on page 58.

Hi Chuck,
Here I am in London, England, doing the sights with my Dad. First, we went to the Tower of London. It's not as big as I thought, but it's really solid - a bit like you really. It was built by William the Conqueror as a home for his pet ravens. The beefeaters (the guards at the tower) wear fancy red outfits and cute hats. Their proper name is Yo-Yo men of the Guard. I think they're called that because they have to stand around all day and play with yo-yos to pass the time.
Will write again soon.
Love,
Patty X

Dear Marcie,
How are you? Wish you were here. It's great fun sightseeing in London Town. Today we went to Trafalgar Square to feed the pigeons. There are HUNDREDS of them. Nelson's Column is mega-tall. The statue of Admiral Nelson at the top is to celebrate his triumph over Napoleon at the Battle of Waterloo. His flagship, HMS Victory, is still around. Dad says we might visit it at Greenwich if we have the time. Must go now. We're off to the Houses of Parliament next.
Lots of Love,
Patty

28

Dear Sally,
 Dad took me to the Houses of Parliament today. Gee, it was boring! It was just like school - lots of talk about things I didn't really understand. It got a bit more interesting when we went to see Gentle Ben, the famous clock at the top.

Our guide told us the name just used to apply to the big bell inside, but now it means the whole clock. How is Chuck? Hope he's not missing me too much.

Lots of Love,
Patty

Hi there, Snoopy,
 I've just come back from a visit to Buckingham Palace. The Queen of England Lives there with all her servants and her little poodle dogs. The soldiers outside are really weird. They wear big furry hats called 'frisbies' that make them look about 10 feet tall, and they march up and down, stamping their huge black boots. I think that's to keep their feet warm. While we were outside, the Prime minister arrived for his weekly audience with the Queen. She must do a show, puppets or something. We're coming home soon. I'll bring you some chocolate chip cookies. Over here, they call them chocolate chip cookies. Ha! Ha!

Love,
Patty

Dearest Chuck,
 It's our last day in London! I shall be sad to leave, but it'll be nice to be home again. You must be itching to see me after all this time. As a final treat, Dad took me to a football match. It was quaint! The players don't wear helmets and shoulder pads like proper footballers; they wear little shorts and run around kicking the ball to each other instead of throwing it. Afterwards, we just had time to hit the shops before catching the plane. I bought you a prezzie - a book called 'Living with stress'. You'll love it. See you tomorrow.

Fondest regards, Patty
xxx

SALLY'S HONEYCOMB PUZZLE

This honeycomb contains 5 well-known words and phrases associated with Snoopy and the Peanuts Gang. Solve the clues at the bottom of the page and then shade in the answers when you find them in the grid. They read in all directions.

One word has been done for you and the solution is on page 58.

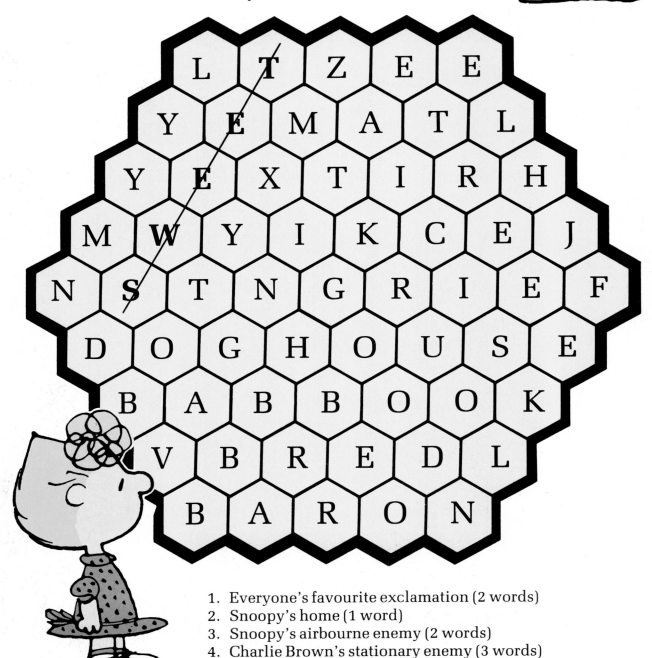

1. Everyone's favourite exclamation (2 words)
2. Snoopy's home (1 word)
3. Snoopy's airbourne enemy (2 words)
4. Charlie Brown's stationary enemy (3 words)
5. Sally's pet name for Linus (3 words)

SNOOPY'S SUNDAY BEST

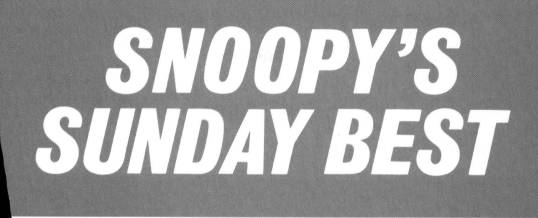

Every week for the past 42 years, Charles Schulz has drawn a PEANUTS Sunday strip. Each one is printed in over 2200 different newspapers in 68 countries around the world, giving a readership of approximately 200 million!

These Sunday strips differ from the weekly PEANUTS strips in that they are nearly three times as long and often tell a complete story. So we asked Charles Schulz if, in all this time, any particular Sunday strips stand out in his memory as being particularly special. Here's his selection . . .

7-5 © 1981 United Feature Syndicate, Inc.

HOW DO YOU GET EVEN WITH AN OCEAN?

33

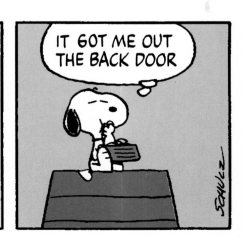

A Gallant and Worthy Foe

Whenever Snoopy the World War 1 flying ace takes to the skies in his trusty Sopwith Camel, he searches for the red Fokker triplane belonging to his old enemy, the Red Baron.

The Red Baron is not an imaginary character; he really existed. His name was Manfred Freiherr Von Richthofen and he was Germany's top pilot during the Great War of 1914-18.

This is the amazing true story of the Baron's last battle.

Picturepoint – London

The Red Baron
(1892-1918)

April 21, 1918. A thick mist hung over the valley of the Somme, grounding the gaudily-painted aircraft on the airfield behind German lines. In the officer's mess, Baron Von Richthofen lounged in his leather armchair, smiling to himself and patting his beloved dog, Moritz. He had good reason to feel pleased. His idea of creating an elite team of crack pilots had been very successful. So had his plan of painting their aircraft a vivid scarlet colour. The mere sight of his famous 'flying circus' struck terror into the enemy. Best of all, the Baron himself had just shot down his 80th Allied aircraft. In the skies above France, where the life-expectancy of a fighter pilot was about two weeks and anyone who destroyed more than ten enemy aircraft was called an 'ace', this total was truly amazing. Von Richthofen and his men were masters of the air.

Later, the Spring sunshine burned off the early morning mist and it became a perfect day for flying. The mechanic who came to tell the Baron that his plane was ready for take-off asked for a signed photograph of the great flyer.

"Don't you think I'll return, then?" laughed the Baron.

"Of course you will," replied the mechanic, hastily. "It's for my son. You're his hero."

With a yank of its wooden propellor, the nine cylinder rotary engine of the Fokker Dr1 spluttered into life. Von Richthofen taxied across the grass and thundered into the air, followed by five of his men. They were looking for RE8s, slow British reconnaissance planes that took photographs of the German trenches. They would be easy targets.

Meanwhile, at an airfield behind British lines, a flight of Sopwith Camels was also roaring skywards. At the controls of two of them were Arthur Brown and Wilfred May, Canadian pilots serving with the RAF. Brown an experienced flyer and leader of the group; May was a novice making his first flight over hostile territory.

"If you get an enemy on your tail," Brown had warned May, "dive down low, zig-zag like crazy and hope to goodness it's not the Red Baron."

Picturepoint – London

A Fokker Triplane

A Sopwith Camel

Picturepoint – London

Later, the Germans found their RE8s and were starting to attack when Brown's men surprised them from above. Instantly, the Fokkers disbanded, using their ability to turn and climb to get out of danger. The battle turned into a series of individual dogfights with pairs of British and German aircraft pursuing each other in all directions. Amidst this noisy, flashing confusion, young Wilfred May struggled to keep his head. Briefly, a German fighter flashed across his sights and he pressed the trigger of his machine-guns. Nothing happened! His guns had jammed!

May knew that his only hope now was to slip away undetected. Several hundred feet above, the sharp eyes of the Red Baron noticed the lone British Camel sneaking home. Like a huge, merciless eagle, Von Richthofen swooped down in pursuit of his prey. Glancing round, the terrified Canadian saw the unmistakable red triplane speeding up behind him. His worst nightmare had come true. He had the Red Baron on his tail and was completely defenceless.

Remembering his leader's advice, May swooped down to a mere 60 metres above the ground and swung his plane from left to right in a desperate attempt to make himself hard to hit. The plan failed. The Red Baron stuck to his tail like glue, and every now and then, a volley of machine gun fire ripped through the flimsy canvas of the Sopwith Camel. It could only be a matter of time before his engine or fuel tank was hit. Wilfred May closed his eyes and waited for the final, knockout blow.

It did not come!

May opened his eyes and, to his amazement, saw the Red Baron's triplane spinning towards the ground. It crashed in the mud behind the Australian trenches. What had happened? May learned afterwards that Arthur Brown had seen the Red Baron pouncing on his young countryman and flew down to help. He had fired at Von Richthofen at the same time as some Australian soldiers in the trenches below had shot their rifles at the low-flying aircraft. To this day, nobody knows which bullet hit Von Richthofen. Brown was credited with the victory, but it may be that a single snap shot from an unknown Australian soldier ended the illustrious career of one of the greatest air aces of all time.

Manfred Von Richthofen's funeral was held the following day. Many British pilots sent flowers to the ceremony. One of the wreaths said:
'To our gallant and worthy foe'.

LINUS'S PHILOSOPHICAL PUZZLE

Can you fit the names of these famous philosophers into the grid? Some letters are already in position to help you. When you have finished, the letters down the middle will spell one of Linus's own philosophical ideas. Solution on page 58.

PLATO
ARISTOTLE
HUME
SPINOZA
RUSSELL
BACON
HEGEL
AQUINAS
SOCRATES
LOCKE
KANT
ROUSSEAU

Snoopy's Hole~in~One

It was a bright and sunny day.
"Come on," called Charlie Brown,
"Let's go and have a game of golf.
It's time we played a round."

Snoopy leapt down from his roof,
His short tail wagging madly.
"Where's Woodstock?" he wondered,
looking round,
"He can be my caddy."

The little bird could not be found,
Though Snoopy searched high and low.
"Hurry, Snoopy," yelled Charlie Brown,
"It's time for us to go."

Snoopy thought, as they neared the course:
"Wouldn't it be *fun*
If, after all these months and years,
I scored a hole-in-one!"

Charlie Brown felt the self-same thing –
"Today will be the day
The golfing gods will smile on you."
Thought Snoopy: "Hip-hooray!"

Snoopy teed off at the first.
He gave the ball a clout.
It landed in a bunker
And he couldn't get it out.

His shot was better at the third,
The ball flew fast and straight.
"That one's too hard," cried Charlie Brown,
"It's landed in the lake."

At the seventh, Snoopy hit
A dreadful, curving loop.
It smashed the clubhouse window
And landed in the soup.

Snoopy thought, as he played the tenth:
"This can't be happening to me!
My latest shot has gone well wide
And landed in a tree!"

Charlie Brown looked on and laughed
As Snoopy heaved and hauled.
"My kite gets caught by the Kite-Eating Tree,
But this one eats golf balls!"

Three holes later, Snoopy's drive
Bounced off a passing truck!
"It is the thirteenth," said Charlie Brown,
"You're bound to have no luck."

At the fifteenth, Snoopy played
A real Nick Faldo stroke,
But the club flew from his paws
And another window broke!

"It's now or never, Snoopy,"
Said good ol' Charlie Brown.
"We're coming to the eighteenth –
That's the last hole of the round."

Snoopy played his final shot
With all his heart and soul.
"Good grief!" he thought, "I do believe
It's heading for the hole!"

On the green, the ball ran true –
Straight as a speeding train.
It reached the hole and disappeared,
AND THEN POPPED OUT AGAIN!

Soon a familiar face emerged,
Like a little yellow mole.
"Woodstock!" Charlie Brown exclaimed.
"He's nesting down the hole!"

Snoopy dropped his golf clubs
And threw his cap away.
"There goes my hole-in-one," he thought.
"Maybe another day!"

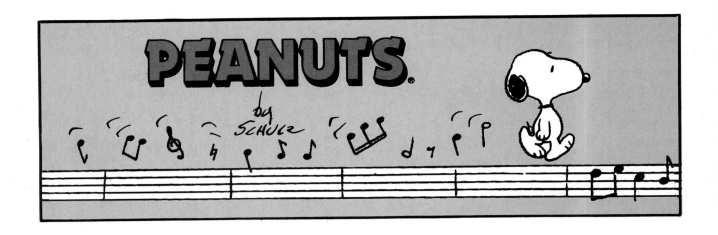

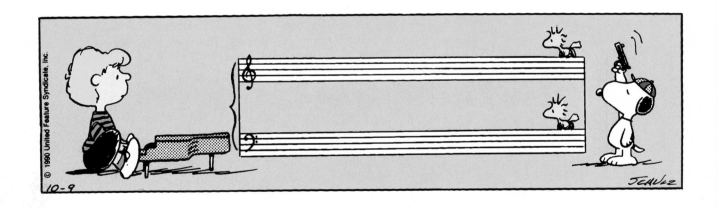

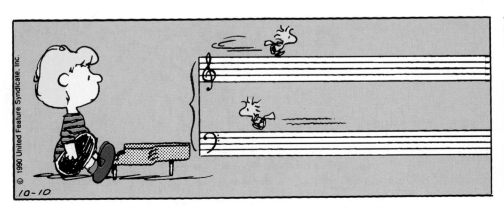

"Losing doesn't matter
as long as you play well,"
is always said by the winners

YOU KNOW, YOU DON'T HAVE TO FLY SOUTH FOR THE WINTER IF YOU DON'T WANT TO...

JUST BECAUSE EVERYONE ELSE IS DOING IT, DOESN'T MEAN YOU HAVE TO..

11-2

I'VE NEVER SEEN ANYONE EAT PIZZA WHILE HE'S ROLLER SKATING BEFORE..

11-10

IT'S OKAY UNTIL THE CHEESE GETS CAUGHT IN THE WHEELS..

ANOTHER ONE OF THOSE WHO DOESN'T TAKE THE GROCERY CART BACK..

11-6

I GUESS IT'S GOING TO BE A NICE DAY AFTER ALL..

HERE, SNOOPY..THE SCHOOL BUS IS COMING..WHY DON'T YOU TAKE MY CAP AND UMBRELLA HOME FOR ME?

BUT YOU DON'T HAVE TO MAKE A BIG DEAL OUT OF IT!

11-14

LUCY'S ADVICE BOOTH

If Charlie Brown and his friends have a problem, they visit Dr. Lucy Van Pelt in her famous psychiatry booth. Here are the transcripts of some of their recent visits.

Charlie Brown: "I'm very worried because I've swallowed the film from my camera. What should I do?"

Lucy: "Sit tight and hope that nothing serious develops."

Sally: "I need help, Dr. Lucy. I keep seeing frogs in front of my eyes!"

Lucy: "Don't worry. It's just a hoptical illusion."

Linus: "I'd like to alter the shape of my nose, but plastic surgery is very expensive. What would you advise me to do?"

Lucy: "Try walking into a wall."

Charlie Brown: "What's wrong with Snoopy? He keeps painting himself gold!"

Lucy: "I think he has a gilt complex."

Schroeder: "I think I've got acute appendicitis."

Lucy: "You haven't — but you've got a cute everything else!"

Peppermint Patty: "Marcie and I are very worried about our pet snakes. My boa constrictor keeps winding itself round her Indian python. Do you think something's wrong?"

Lucy: "No. I reckon they've just got a crush on each other."

Peppermint Patty: "Ever since I visited England, I've been mad on cricket. How's that?"

Lucy: "Not out!"

Schroeder: "Pressing my piano pedals all day has given me water on the knee. What's the cure? Don't say a tap on the head!"

Lucy: "I wouldn't dream of saying that!"

Schroeder: "What do you advise, then?"

Lucy: "Wear drainpipe trousers."

Linus: "Why does my pet glow worm keep crawling across the main road?"

Lucy: "I expect he's not very bright."

Charlie Brown: "I'm such a failure, Dr. Lucy. What do you think I should be when I grow up?"

Lucy: "An archaeologist. Then your career could be in ruins."

Sally: "When I grow up, I want to work as a manicurist and marry Linus. Do you think that's a good idea?"

Lucy: "How does Linus feel about it?"

Sally: "My sweet babboo hasn't said he's going to marry me yet. He wants to be a dentist."

Lucy: "Then I wouldn't advise you to get married."

Sally: "Why not?"

Lucy: "You'd only fight tooth and nail!"

Peppermint Patty: "How can I get my teacher to compliment me on my schoolwork?"

Lucy: "Do some."

51

SNOOPY'S ALL AMERICAN FAVOURITES

Snoopy's passion for chocolate-chip cookies, jam doughnuts and ginger beer is very well documented, but he is equally fond of anything that is sweet and full of calories. So here are the recipes for two of Snoopy's traditional American favourites that you can make yourself.

MOM'S APPLE PIE

Ingredients
225g (8oz) plain flour
110g (4oz) margarine
110g (4oz) brown sugar
450g (1lb) cooking apples
½ teaspoon salt
Cold water to mix
Milk to glaze
4 cloves (optional)

Method

1. Sift the flour and salt into a basin. Cut the margarine into pieces and rub in with your fingertips. The finished mixture should look like fine breadcrumbs.

2. Add a little cold water to bind the mixture, stirring with a metal spoon. When you have stiff dough, knead lightly with your knuckles until the dough becomes smooth.

3. Sprinkle some flour onto your work surface, remove the dough from the bowl and roll flat with a rolling-pin. Set aside for later.

4. Peel the cooking apples, remove the cores and cut into slices.

5. Preheat the oven to 200°C/425°F/Gas mark 7.

6. Cut the pastry in half, roll it flat and use it to line the bottom of an 18cm/7in pie dish. Cover with the apple slices and sprinkle on all the sugar. Also add the cloves if you want them.

7. Roll out the other half of the pastry and lay it over the top of the pie making sure you have wetted the edges so that the two halves will seal properly. Slice off any excess pastry and press the edges together.

8. Brush the top of the pie with milk and bake in the middle of the oven for 30-40 minutes until the pastry is golden brown. Serve with cream, ice-cream or both! (If you want to be *truly* American, serve with thinly sliced cheese instead.)

CHOCOLATE BROWNIES

Ingredients

110g (4oz) plain flour
110g (4oz) plain chocolate
110g (4oz) butter
110g (4oz) chopped walnuts
225g (8oz) caster sugar
2 eggs
½ teaspoon baking powder
pinch of salt

Method

1. Preheat the oven to 180°C/350°F/ Gas mark 4.

2. Lightly grease a shallow, oblong baking tin (approx 18×28cm/ 7×11in).

3. Break the chocolate up into pieces and put it in a bowl. Add the butter. Place the butter over a saucepan of gently simmering water and leave to melt.

4. When the mixture has melted, remove from the heat and stir in the flour, the sugar, the walnuts, the baking powder and the salt. Beat the eggs together and stir them in too. You should end up with a thick, shiny mixture.

5. Spread the mixture around the baking tin and put in the oven for about 30 minutes.

6. Remove from oven and allow to cool for 10 minutes. (Don't worry if the mixture sinks a bit.) Cut the brownies into squares and allow them to finish cooling on a wire rack. They should be crispy on the top and a little sticky in the middle. If there are any left after sampling, keep them in an airtight tin!

WARNING

Please don't attempt to make either of these dishes without a grown-up present.

You should never use the kitchen on your own.

Dear Santa Claus, I demand that you bring me the following items this year.

THAT'S PRETTY STRONG LANGUAGE, ISN'T IT?

Please.

11-23

HERE.. YOUR LETTER CAME BACK MARKED "INSUFFICIENT ADDRESS"

"INSUFFICIENT"?! LOOK WHAT I WROTE...

"SANTA CLAUS.. NORTH POLE.. WHEREVER THAT IS.. ZIP CODE.. WHO KNOWS? PLEASE FORWARD..WHY NOT?"

MAYBE YOU SHOULD UNDERLINE ALL THE WORDS AND PUT IN SOME HYPHENS..

11-24

IF YOU'RE A REAL SANTA CLAUS, WHERE ARE YOUR REINDEER?

11-27

I KNOW WHAT I SHOULD HAVE SAID... I SHOULD HAVE SAID, "I GOT HUNGRY LAST WINTER SO I ATE THEM!"

There's nothing funnier than knockabout humour, unless you're the one being knocked about!

IF YOU'RE WRITING TO GRAMMA, THANK HER FOR THE SCARF AND THE BOOKS..

WOULD YOU LIKE TO ADD ANYTHING?

12-26

MARCIE, WHAT BOOK WERE WE SUPPOSED TO READ DURING THANKSGIVING VACATION?

12-27

THIS IS CHRISTMAS VACATION, SIR..

CHRISTMAS VACATION?! HOW CAN I READ SOMETHING DURING CHRISTMAS VACATION WHEN I DIDN'T READ WHAT I WAS SUPPOSED TO READ DURING THANKSGIVING VACATION?

DUCK, SIR! EASTER IS COMING!!

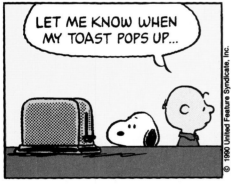

LET ME KNOW WHEN MY TOAST POPS UP...

12-28

ALREADY? THANK YOU..

I'VE NEVER SEEN ANYBODY SO COMPLETELY USELESS!

HAVE YOU ANY IDEA WHAT YOU'RE GOING TO DO WITH THE REST OF YOUR LIFE?

I'VE BEEN THINKING OF GIVING SLEEPING LESSONS..

12-29

ANSWERS

Kids Stuff *(Pages 14 and 15)*

1. (a) 5
2. Julian, Dick, George, Anne and Timmy
3. (b) Romulus and Remus
4. (a) True
5. (c) Huckleberry Finn
6. (c) Princess Anne
7. Peter Pan
8. (a) The Artful Dodger
9. (b) Lord Shaftesbury
10. Father
11. (b) False. (It was King Arthur)
12. (b) Lucy and Linus

Charlie Brown's Find The Gang Puzzle *(Page 24)*

F	D	M	X	B	R	Z	L	M	V
H	O	Z	P	W	T	S	J	A	P
S	C	H	R	O	E	D	E	R	I
N	P	V	E	O	Y	L	N	C	G
O	B	G	W	D	M	U	X	I	P
O	L	C	K	S	H	C	R	E	E
P	I	P	A	T	T	Y	H	Z	N
Y	N	S	N	O	V	M	U	P	F
D	U	R	W	C	S	A	L	L	Y
N	S	P	I	K	E	J	M	U	W

Postcards From Patty
(Pages 28 and 29)

Postcard 1
(a) The ravens came to live at the Tower of London long after it was built
(b) The Beefeaters are called Yeomen Of The Guard

Postcard 2
(a) Admiral Nelson fought at the Battle of Trafalgar
(b) HMS Victory is in Portsmouth

Postcard 3
(a) The clock on the Houses of Parliament is Big Ben

Postcard 4
(a) The Queen keeps corgi dogs
(b) The soldiers' hats are called Busbies
(c) The Prime Minister's audience with the Queen is a meeting about affairs of State

Postcard 5
(a) Patty is confusing American football with British soccer

Sally's Honeycomb Puzzle *(Page 30)*

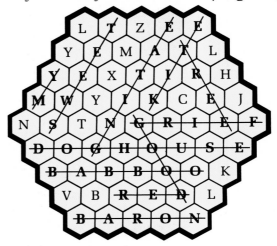

Linus's Philosophical Puzzle *(Page 40)*

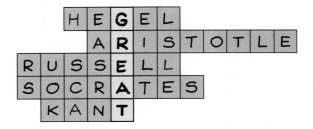

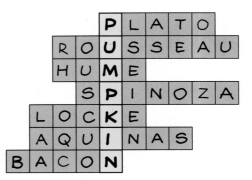

PRISONER, Kennel Block H

"There's something going on here!" thought Snoopy. Charlie Brown had not been out to say "good morning", there was a lot of commotion in the house and Sally kept going backwards and forwards to the car. Eventually, Charlie Brown appeared with a packet of chocolate-chip cookies in his hand.

"These are for you, Snoopy," he said.

Snoopy eyed them suspiciously.

"There's no such thing as free chocolate-chip cookies," he thought.

Snoopy's suspicions proved correct. Charlie Brown broke the news that he and Sally were having a winter holiday.

"We're going skiing," he explained.

Snoopy pricked up his ears on hearing this.

"I *love* skiing," he thought.

"You're not coming, Snoopy," added Charlie Brown. "With all our skiing gear, there isn't room for you in the car."

Snoopy's ears dropped and a shiver ran down his spine.

"That means . . ." he thought.

"That means," said Charlie Brown, holding out his hands apologetically, "you have to go into kennels."

Not long afterwards, Snoopy found himself behind bars. It was all very pleasant at the kennels. He had a room of his own, a comfy basket to lie in, plenty of food and the promise of a walk every afternoon. Nevertheless, he was a prisoner!

"A week in here is going to seem like the Middle Ages," he thought, miserably.

Snoopy decided to sleep the time away, so he curled up in the basket and drifted off into a dream in which he was running free through a meadow towards a mountain of jam-filled doughnuts. When he woke up, only 30 minutes had passed.

"10,075 still to go," he sighed.

Just then, there was a knock on the door and Peppermint Patty was shown in. Snoopy stood up, wagging his tail excitedly.

"I haven't come to take you home, Snoopy," said Patty, holding out a piece of paper. "Chuck asked me to stop by and give you this."

"The Ski Lodge Hotel . . ." read Snoopy.

"It's his holiday address," explained Patty, "in case you want to write to him. Must dash now. I'm late for a concert with Marcie."

Snoopy watched her go with a little wave of his paw.

"Have fun!" he thought.

Returning to his basket, Snoopy tried to think of a way to escape.

"I saw a film once," he said to himself, "in which some prisoners of war tunnelled out of a camp underneath a gymnasium vaulting horse."

Snoopy looked round his room.

"Trouble is," he added, "the floor's made of concrete and I don't have a vaulting horse."

Snoopy also discovered that the walls were made of solid blocks, the windows were barred and the door was covered with thick wire mesh and securely bolted.

"Think I'll stay here and wait for lunch," murmured Snoopy.

During the afternoon, the kennel-maid came to give Snoopy his walk. As they passed the main gate, the girl was called to the telephone. She tied Snoopy's lead to the gatepost, saying she would be back in a minute.

"Now's my chance!" thought Snoopy.

The other dogs in the kennels would not have been able to untie a knot in a lead, but Snoopy was a Scoutmaster and his practiced paws soon had the leather thong undone. Crouching low, he passed under the reception office window without being spotted and made his way out of the gate. Once in the street, he threw his arms in the air and ran round and round in circles of joy.

"I'm free!" he whooped.

"I'M FREE!"

Snoopy set off for home.

"Those chocolate-chip cookies Charlie Brown gave me are still in my doghouse," chuckled Snoopy. "I can hear them calling me."

The thought of a tasty snack put spring in the beagle's stride, but as one dreary street gave way to another, Snoopy began to slow down.

"I'm hot and tired," he thought, "and thirsty."

Rounding the corner, Snoopy saw a delivery van parked at the kerb. It contained some half-empty bottles of ginger beer returned from a shop.

"Bliss!" thought Snoopy, leaping on board. He downed the left-over drinks in a trice. Then he saw the driver coming out towards his cab.

"This truck's pointing in the direction of Charlie Brown's house," he grinned. "I'll stay on board and hitch a ride."

With a contented sigh, the stowaway settled back with his paws behind his head and closed his eyes.

"Home, James," he smiled, "and don't spare the ginger beer!"

When Snoopy opened his eyes again, he found the delivery van hurtling along a country road.

"This isn't the right way," gasped Snoopy. "We're heading *out* of town."

As the truck sped on, the air grew colder and colder and Snoopy spotted some snow-capped peaks in the distance.

"Oh, great!" he groaned. "Next delivery's in the mountains."

Snoopy closed his eyes as the full realisation of his plight dawned on him.

"I'm going to end up miles from home with nothing to eat and nowhere to stay," he thought. "I may never see Charlie Brown or the others again!"

Meanwhile, in his hotel room, Charlie Brown sat at the window, looking miserably out at the people enjoying themselves in the snow.

"Oh, come on, Charlie Brown," cried Sally. "You can't spend all your holiday moping because Snoopy's in the kennels."

"I miss him," sighed Charlie Brown.

"Cheer up," said Sally, putting her hand on her brother's arm. "I expect, at this very minute, Snoopy's snoring in his dog basket with a stomach full of food."

In fact, at that very minute, Snoopy stood shivering in the snow with his stomach rumbling like Mount Krakatoa. The van had stopped at the Ski Lodge Hotel to make its next delivery.

"Where have I heard that name before?" thought Snoopy, gazing up at the rows of windows. Suddenly, he caught sight of a familiar face looking down from one of them.

"The Round-Headed Kid!" gasped Snoopy.

"SNOOPY!" yelled Charlie Brown.

Dog and master greeted each other in a frenzy of joyful hugs.

"You're not going back to those horrible kennels," cried Charlie Brown. "You're staying here with us."

"Suits me," thought Snoopy.

Next day, Snoopy was out on the ski-slopes with Charlie Brown, Sally and the rest of the gang who had come out on a day-visit.

"Did you get here by bus, Snoopy?" asked Peppermint Patty, whizzing past on her skis.

"No," thought Snoopy, speeding after her, "I got here by luck!"